FIVE GO
DOWN UNDER

Enid Blyton

FIVE GO DOWN UNDER

Text by
Sophie Hamley

Enid Blyton for Grown-Ups

Quercus

First published in Great Britain in 2017 by

Quercus Editions Ltd
Carmelite House
50 Victoria Embankment
London EC4Y 0DZ

An Hachette UK company

A CIP catalogue record for this book is available
from the British Library

ISBN 978 1 78747 192 4

Text by Sophie Hamley
Original illustrations by Eileen A. Soper
Cover illustration by Ruth Palmer

10 9 8 7 6 5 4 3 2 1

Printed and bound in Great Britain by Clays Ltd, St Ives plc

CHAPTER ONE

Out of Sorts

Life was continuing much as it always had for Julian, Anne, Dick and George. They were enjoying each other's company, and taking Timmy for the occasional walk when the winter weather permitted. The short, cold days were, however, mainly conducive to chats around the kitchen table with the bar heater at their feet and a glass of wine in hand.

'Should we buy another heater?' Anne mused as she wondered how their little appliance had ended up next to Julian's feet, so no one else could feel any warmth.

'That would involve a car journey,' George said with a heavy sigh.

'True,' Anne said resignedly, and she decided she should knit herself extra-warm socks instead. It was one of many resolutions she had made about winter.

Indeed, they had all vowed to use the coldest season to undertake tasks they had put off during warmer months. Their words had been full of vigour and they'd hoped their

1

'Is there any more of that Roquefort?' Dick said.

CONTENTS

actions would match them. Now, in late February, it was clear that all those hopes had been in vain.

'Is there any more of that Roquefort?' Dick said. He wasn't usually given to extravagances, but permitted himself the odd French cheese. 'It was jolly well delicious.'

'No, Timmy ate it,' Julian said with a hint of amusement. He'd initially been cross when he'd discovered the theft – Timmy knew how fond they *all* were of the Roquefort – but then he came to understand: who has not, on occasion, wanted to ruin someone else's fun? Indeed, even now Timmy did not seem to feel any guilt about his actions. If anything, he appeared to be suffering from the same underlying malaise as the rest of them. The winter blues, some might call it.

'And that's the last of the wine,' George said, filling her glass.

'No wine *and* no cheese?' said Julian, whose imagination struggled to conjure up a worse combination of events, his earlier sympathy for Timmy fast disappearing.

Anne shook her head sadly, for she knew that the stocks were unlikely to be replenished quickly. It was cold outside, and raining, and their local shop had recently closed down so an urban gin distillery could open in its place. Accordingly, the five tended to let supplies dwindle until they were desperately low, at which point they would be forced to gird their loins, pile into the car and spend five hours navigating Tesco.

'How can you have let him do this to us?' Julian said to George. 'We would have more cheese if only Timmy hadn't selfishly eaten a massive slab of it!'

'It's not his fault,' George said grumpily. 'He's a dog. He doesn't know what he's doing.'

Under the table, Timmy put his head on his paws and hoped that George would never guess the truth: that he did, in fact, know what he was doing.

'It's like having a permanent toddler,' Julian said with a scowl. 'Smashing, grabbing, taking. We should put him in a play pen.'

At this Timmy got to his feet. If they were planning to incarcerate him, he really should remove himself. He started to slink away just as Anne emitted a sigh.

'Don't be so dramatic,' she said.

'Yes,' Dick said with as much force as he could muster. 'Don't.'

'It's not as if you need the cheese,' George said with a pointed glance at Julian's belly. They all knew he'd been getting fatter – his fondness for booze combined with a complete unwillingness to temper his diet or to exercise had made him positively porky.

4

Julian narrowed his eyes. 'I suppose it *is* too much drama for a Saturday afternoon,' he said, deciding to ignore George's remark. 'I'm just so sick of this weather. It is so dull. Almost as if the sun will never appear again.'

'We should go somewhere tropical!' Anne said brightly.

'Marbella?' Dick said hopefully. Not that long ago he had thought he might join other friends on a trip to this very spot but he had, instead, ended up in Dorset with his housemates. And the Secret Seven, he remembered with a small shudder.

Now George was fixing him with a look of disapproval. She really did seem to be more disgruntled than usual this winter.

'Absolutely not,' she said. 'It's full of English people losing their inhibitions. We can go to the Glastonbury Festival if we want to see that.'

'And Spain is for short holidays,' said Julian, visibly warming up to the idea of a vacation. 'We're in a rut. I think we need something ... more fundamental.'

He was met by three perplexed faces.

'What do you mean?' said Dick.

'Yes, what on earth?' echoed Anne.

'You can't ...' George stopped.

'Yes, I can,' Julian said firmly, standing up to make his point, his chin lifting ever so slightly. 'We need to take a gap year.'

'A gap year?' Anne looked at Dick, then George, then Timmy, whose tail started to wag. 'A whole year? What about our jobs?'

'We'll get new ones when we return,' Julian said, perennially confident that his degree in English Literature from Oxford would always keep him in clover.

'And where, exactly, will this gap year take place?' George said.

Julian regarded her with a certain smugness that they had all learnt to live with, if not to love.

'Australia,' he said. 'Where else would young English people go to waste time?'

'Australia,' Anne said with a note of wonder. 'Yes! How marvellous! That's absolutely warm enough to shake us out of these doldrums.'

Dick was looking especially pleased, although George was frowning.

'What about Timmy?' she said.

'He can go in the cargo hold,' said Julian.

'Woof!' said Timmy, getting to his feet. 'Woof! Woof!'

'I don't think he'll like that,' George said.

'Too bad,' said Julian. 'That's the only way he can come with us. At any rate, I think we should all resign our jobs on Monday and start packing. We can sublet the flat – or

'Australia,' he said. 'Where else would young English
people go to waste time?'

maybe Aunt Fanny and Uncle Quentin would like to use it for city escapes.'

At this, George looked confused. 'Escaping what?'

'Never mind,' said Julian. 'We'll sort it out. So we're agreed?'

'Yes,' said Anne, her cheeks flushed with exuberance. 'Yes, yes!'

Dick nodded vigorously and they all watched as Timmy turned in circles, although none of them could decide if it was from excitement or dismay. Regardless, he was coming with them. They just needed to go to Australia House and organise his papers.

It was extraordinary, really, that all they required to embark on a new adventure was a little bit of life administration: quitting jobs, checking passports, subleasing their flat, telling their friends they were leaving, getting drunk down the pub at their farewell do. It was enough to make them wonder why they hadn't tried it before – and enough to make them feel quite grown-up.

'So are we ready?' Anne said, looking at the passports fanned out on the kitchen table and the suitcases lined up next to the door. Aunt Fanny and Uncle Quentin were about to arrive to take their keys.

'Not quite,' Julian said, inspecting his pale hands. 'I forgot to get a fake tan.'

'Oh, Julian,' George said crossly. 'No one is going to care if you're pale.'

'But *I* will care,' he said. He wanted to impress as many people as possible once he was on Bondi Beach, and although he hadn't quite managed to shed his winter weight, a good tan could hide a multitude of sins.

'Then get one when we're in Australia,' George said just as there was a knock at the door.

Shortly they were off to the airport and then on to the land where summer was, apparently, eternal and everyone flattened their vowels.

CHAPTER TWO

In the Antipodes

Their progress through Australian Customs stalled only by what George judged to be unreasonable questions – *Of course* they had recently been in the countryside, for what was Dorset, after all? And what did it matter if they had dirt on their shoes? – Julian, Dick, George and Anne bustled their luggage trolleys out into freedom as quickly as they could. They were all eager to check that Timmy had been safely transported to Quarantine, where, apparently, he could expect to spend six to ten weeks.

'It sounds like a penal sentence,' George complained to the others.

'How appropriate,' Julian said with a snort.

'That's unfair,' Anne said with uncharacteristic force. 'Australia is a proper country now.'

'We'll be the judges of that,' Julian replied, pushing a trolley laden with his monogrammed school chest and Dick's duffel bag.

'That's unfair,' Anne said with uncharacteristic force.
'Australia is a proper country now.'

They pressed on towards the part of the airport where they'd been told to enquire. Dick turned his head rapidly from side to side, trying to find the right doorway. Anne sailed past the young men whose mouths hung open as they noticed how beautiful she was. Julian sucked in his belly as he passed a mirror in a shop window, and George charged straight ahead, heedless of small children who strayed too near her trolley's wheels.

'Stop!' George cried as they passed a man in a chauffeur's peaked hat holding a sign saying '*Packer – party of 1*'.

Next to the man was Timmy, sitting on his haunches, regarding them with an expression that looked remarkably like derision.

'Woof!' said Timmy, and Dick's face lit up.

'They let you out early, old fellow!' Dick exclaimed.

'He's yours, is he?' the hatted man said, squinting at each of them and their luggage in turn. Then he winked. 'Getting him out Pistol style, eh?'

'Pistol?' said Anne, her lovely forehead wrinkling.

'And Boo.' The man winked again.

'Boo who?' Julian said, not enjoying a word game he hadn't invented.

'Yeah, that's right. I got you.' The man winked again. 'Good luck with that, eh? Better scoop him up before anyone dobs you in.'

'Dob?' said Julian, growing increasingly frustrated just as a tall, solidly built man wearing what appeared to be a cashmere tracksuit approached them.

'Mr Packer.' The hatted man seemed to genuflect and George seized the opportunity, grabbing Timmy by the collar and walking briskly away, barely checking to see if the others were following.

'What happened?' Julian said under his breath, struggling to keep pace with his cousin, who was now trying to cram Timmy between her suitcases so no one would see him.

'I don't know,' George replied in a tone that suggested further enquiries would not be welcome.

'Do you think he's allowed out?' Dick said. 'I mean – what about six to ten weeks?'

'Not such a penal colony after all,' Anne said chirpily, trotting to catch up with George.

The glass doors of the arrivals hall opened and immediately they were hit with the blazing heat and energy-sapping humidity of Sydney in late summer.

'Julian!' George said sternly. 'It's bloody hot!'

'Hmm?' Julian said, sweeping his lank fringe to one side as his cheeks turned a tomato-esque shade. 'Well, Anne suggested a tropical holiday.'

'This isn't the tropics,' George retorted. 'It's a pressure cooker!'

13

*'Let's just get to Bondi and into our bathers and a long
swim will sort it out.'*

'Yes, it's summer. That's what we wanted, wasn't it?' Julian emitted an exaggerated sigh. 'Let's just get to Bondi and into our bathers and a long swim will sort it out.'

As he waved his arm in the direction of the taxi rank, heedless of the large sign indicating that queuing was required, his brother, sister and cousin tried to ignore the trickles of sweat coursing down their bodies. They had all wanted a change from the dark winter days of home, and now they certainly had it. They didn't even have to wait for Timmy to join them. All five could start their adventure right away. If only they knew what Julian had planned for them.

CHAPTER THREE

Not Quite by the Seaside

The relief that the four of them (five, including Timmy) had felt when they managed to leave the airport undetected by Quarantine officials gave way to dismay when they reached their accommodations in the famous Sydney beachside suburb of Bondi.

Julian's school friend Bertie Champion-Webster, who had moved to Sydney two years ago in pursuit of a woman he had described as 'a fine filly', had assured Julian that he'd found them the perfect abode.

'Fabulous place,' he'd said. 'Two storeys. Right near the beach. Ocean views.'

Given that Julian thought Bertie's girlfriend was a long way from being either fine or a filly, he realised, too late, that he should have taken his friend's description with a grain of salt.

The house was twenty minutes' walk from the beach and not in sight of any body of water. It was ramshackle, and the front door didn't appear to close, let alone lock. At least one window was broken, and foot-high grass poked through the dilapidated fence.

Worse still, there were only two bedrooms available; the rest were occupied by New Zealanders who left their surfboards in the hallways and assorted surfing accoutrement draped over every other available surface.

'Bro,' one of them said to Julian when introduced, his rugby-player-sized neck bulging as he grasped Julian's hand. Feeling his arm about to be wrenched out of its socket, Julian ended the handshake immediately.

'I'm Neil,' the man said, turning to Dick and clapping him on the shoulder, causing him to stumble. 'This is my brother Tum.' He jerked a thumb towards a younger man who was entering the room wearing a tan, an All Blacks jersey and board shorts slung low on his hips. Julian's quick decoding of Neil's accent meant that he realised the man's name was actually Tim.

'Cuzzy bro,' said Tim as he attempted to take Dick's hand while Dick, unusually quick to catch on, kept his hand to himself.

'So, bro,' said Neil as he faced Julian, crossing his arms in such a way that his biceps bulged out of a rather tight singlet that bore the legend *Welcome to Middle Earth*. 'You here for a while?'

17

Julian realised that 'bro' must be Neil's verbal tic rather than a word peculiar to the Kiwi patois and decided not to ask for a translation.

Just then Anne and George appeared in the doorway, hauling the rest of Julian's luggage up the stairs, and Neil's and Tim's faces lit up.

'Girls, bro!' said Tim with what could only be called a squeal.

'My sister,' Julian said warningly, 'and my cousin.'

'I'm hardly a girl,' George was heard to grumble as Anne turned on a winning smile.

'Would you mind helping us with our luggage?' she said to Tim.

'Oh, I'll do that,' Dick said cheerfully, attempting to lift Julian's school chest and failing to notice Anne's crestfallen glance.

'Jist up the stairs, yih?' Neil said, and Julian felt another urge to ask for a translation. Perhaps 'yih' was a synonym for 'yes'. He would observe these New Zealand fellows and work it out for himself.

Tim sidled up to Anne. 'Come on,' he said, 'I'll take you to meet Jonty.'

'Who?' said George, puffing as she removed her woollen vest and rolled up her shirtsleeves.

'The South African who luves in a tent, eh,' Neil said.

At this news, Anne and George turned to look at Julian just as they heard a thud overhead. Poor Dick.

Julian avoided Anne's gaze; he never liked to see that she was disappointed in him. This house was not at all what Bertie had led them to believe, true, but they had nowhere else to go, for now. They'd have to make the best of it. Anne was good at doing that. She'd be all right. Now he just had to manage George.

'Woof!' said Timmy as he ran inside from the front garden.

'A dog, bro?' said Neil, shaking his head at Julian. 'No dogs, bro.' He nodded at Tim, whose grin returned.

'I'm allergic, eh,' Tim said.

Neil nodded. 'Allergic, bro.'

'Quite,' said Julian, sighing. What could they do with Timmy?

'It is a *medhouse* out there but I managed to pork the core at last,' boomed a voice from the back of the house, then a mountain-sized man wearing cricket whites ducked his head to enter the room.

'Thus us Jonty,' said Neil. 'It's a madhouse out there but he's parked the car.'

'Ah,' said Julian, pleased that someone else had translated for him. He had not prepared himself to be presented with so many dialects of English in one day.

19

'A snag? A barbie?' Julian had absolutely no idea what he was talking about.

'A dog!' Jonty said, bending down from his massive height to scratch Timmy's head. George was astounded to see Timmy rolling over onto his back, his paws in the air. Normally he only did that if she bribed him.

'He'll have to come out the back with me,' Jonty said, straightening up. 'Tim's allergic. Come on, boy. I have biltong!'

At this Timmy rolled onto his feet with more energy than his age would suggest and scampered out towards the back garden as Neil gazed after him.

'Time for a barbie later, eh? Maybe the dog would like a snag.' He looked almost sad. 'Maybe the dog could be my friend then,' he muttered softly.

'A snag? A barbie?' Julian had absolutely no idea what he was talking about and Neil could tell.

'A sausage,' Neil said, shaking his head as if Julian was a small child. 'And a bar-bee-kew. Heard of those, bro?'

'Barbie, bro,' said Tim, nodding vigorously. 'Gotta throw a snag on the barbie. That's what the Aussies all do.'

'Not that we're Aussies,' Neil said quickly. 'That is absolutely not a Kylie Minogue song playing on Tum's iPod. We only like Dave Dobbyn, Kiri Te Kanawa and Split Enz.'

Tim nodded even more vigorously in agreement. 'And John Farnham.'

'All right, then,' said George, getting impatient with this ridiculous small talk.

Anne took the cue, and the handle of her suitcase. 'Timmy has a place to sleep – we should find ours,' she said, smiling so sweetly that Neil and Tim took a few seconds to respond.

'Up here,' Neil said. 'Two to a room, yih?'

Julian was sure that he saw a glint in Neil's eye but the moment was lost as he tripped over the rather large hole in one of the stairs.

'Hole, bro!' Tim said unnecessarily, and once again Julian cursed his foolishness at taking Bertie's accommodation advice.

CHAPTER FOUR

Neil's Jandals Go Missing

'I haven't seen a single kangaroo,' Dick said forlornly as they stood on the path that hugged the cliff between Bondi and Tamarama beaches, while sweaty locals ran past them in pristine activewear. 'I was told there would be kangaroos.'

In fact, Dick had been told nothing of the sort, but that didn't stop him being convinced that these long-lashed and occasionally aggressive hopping creatures were to be found on every corner, and quite often bounding after cars down suburban streets.

'Oh darling,' Anne said, squeezing his arm. 'I haven't seen any koalas either.'

'What did you expect?' said Julian. 'We're in the *city*. The only wild creatures here are—'

'Those English backpackers who tried to get you to dance last night,' said George with a glint of amusement in her eyes. She, Anne and Dick had all enjoyed the sight of Julian consuming far too many black Sambuca shots

*Julian pretended to ignore the remark, even if he couldn't
ignore his hangover.*

in the hope of impressing two girls who instead ended up drinking him under the table.

Julian pretended to ignore the remark, even if he couldn't ignore his hangover.

'I was going to say *kookaburras*,' he said, enjoying the fruits of his research into Australian native fauna. 'Horrible creatures,' he continued. 'They keep looking at me as if they're going to eat me.'

'Woof!' said Timmy, meaning he either agreed with Julian or that he, too, wanted to eat him.

It had been another day of trying to find their feet in this land Down Under, and discussing whether or not they should remain in the share house. They had given it a go, but they weren't sure that Tim and Neil were the best fit.

Both of them went to work early – one as a 'tradie', as he called it, the other as a 'UX designer', whatever that was – leaving their surfing paraphernalia everywhere. When they returned in the afternoons they would take their surfboards and head for the ocean, to surf until something they called 'shark o'clock', then they'd sit in the back garden with an acoustic guitar and sing pop songs, badly, long into the night. Occasionally Jonty would join in, his baritone never quite in accord with their light tenor tones.

Sleep was almost impossible while this awkward combination was in progress, and especially hard to come by when Neil and Tim loudly extolled the dominance of their national rugby team and how the Wallabies would never win the Bledisloe Cup ever again, interspersed with even louder stories about how regular the shark alarms had been lately. This last item of conversation left Dick, in particular, wide awake in fear.

Still, it wasn't the noise they minded so much as a baffling behavioural pattern that had emerged towards the end of the five's first week in the house.

'Who's stolen my jandals?' Neil said loudly that Saturday morning as they were all in the kitchen.

'Your what?' George had said as she attempted to make a pot of tea. She had been agitating for a move away from the house since she had discovered that biltong was bad for dogs. She couldn't keep Timmy away from Jonty – they had 'bonded', as Neil had observed with what sounded like envy – and she couldn't stop Jonty giving him biltong. The solution was to remove Timmy from the situation altogether.

'My *jandals*,' Neil said, looking at each of them pointedly, his accusatory expression only softening when he reached Anne.

'I'm sorry, Neil,' she said. 'We don't know what those are.'

He pointed to his feet. 'My *jandals*,' he said again, with more force.

26

Sleep was almost impossible while this awkward
combination was in progress.

'Oh, your flip-flops,' Julian said airily. 'They're out the back. Where you left them.' He had noticed that Neil and Tim kept all their footwear by the back door; the mystery was that neither of them seemed to realise it.

Neil smiled and shrugged. 'Oops,' he said, and ambled towards the rear of the house.

'Who's been in my *chully bun*!' came a cry from that same rear. *'Aginn!'*

'No one's been in your chilly bin again, Tim,' Dick called. He had learnt to keep his tone light ever since he'd realised that Neil's and Tim's seemingly amiable exteriors masked a roiling rage that could be triggered by anyone who asked them if they were Australian. Given that Bondi was full of international tourists, many of whom hoped to meet Crocodile Dundee, this scenario seemed to occur on a daily basis.

'And taken my Weezledog DickleDoi Imperial Ruby Ale!' Now Tim sounded like someone was strangling him. He had made a point of telling them all how he'd ordered his favourite craft beer from New Zealand, and Julian had made a point of not telling him that he'd been sampling the wares.

'Have any of you worked out what the chilly bin is?' George whispered.

'Oh darling,' Anne said with a tinkling laugh, 'it's a little ice chest.'

'Right,' George said uncomprehendingly. 'What do they do with it?'

'It doesn't matter,' Julian said, standing up from the kitchen table. 'We're leaving.'

'Excellent,' George said as she, too, got to her feet. 'I'll fetch Timmy.'

'Wait, darling,' said Anne. 'Where are we going, Julian?'

'I've found another place. A proper place of our own.' He lifted his smartphone close to his face. He really should find an optometrist – it was getting harder and harder to read on that piffling little device, even when he enlarged the text. Old age, he supposed. The price of being the senior partner in their little tribe. Along with all the responsibility he had to take—

'Julian?' George interrupted his thoughts.

'Oh yes. Right.' He squinted at the screen. 'It's in North Bondi. "Renovator's delight," it says. "Period features. One bathroom, no ensuite." And it's lucky we don't have a car as there is no off-street parking.' He grinned with uncharacteristic glee. 'Best of all, the place is available right away. And otherwise empty.'

'How did you find it?' said George. She did not want to hear that Bertie Champion-Webster was somehow responsible.

'It's on CloudRnR.' Julian held out his phone so she could see; he was somewhat proud of his ability to find

29

It transpired that none of them had unpacked their suitcases when they moved in.

things online despite the challenge of the font size. 'I'm told it's where everyone finds their accommodation these days.'

'Jolly good show,' Dick said rather more rambunctiously than usual. 'I don't think I can listen to Neil and Tim murdering "Wonderwall" any more.'

'And they started slagging off Jonny Wilkinson last night,' Julian said, affronted.

'So we can go now?' said Anne hopefully.

'I'd say so,' said Julian.

It transpired that none of them had unpacked their suitcases when they moved in – perhaps in expectation of Julian's eventual masterstroke – so the only complicated part of their withdrawal from the share house was the extraction of Timmy from Jonty's tent. Only George's promise of a raw steak and a run along the beach convinced Timmy to follow them up the hill to their new abode.

31

CHAPTER FIVE

Five meet Six

Thankfully the five's new home in North Bondi had a water view from the corner of a bathroom window. And it was helpfully close to cafés offering all sorts of superfood smoothies – bee pollen, chia seeds, açai berries and coconut oil were very popular round these parts – as well as many ways to eat kale (as chips, which sounded improbable, as well as in something called 'green brekky bowls') and a ubiquitous dish called 'smashed avo on sourdough toast', additional feta or hard-boiled egg optional.

The first time they ventured out to the nearest café, Burnt Sugar Love Goddess Gratitude, almost all of them were confounded by the items listed on the menu. Only Anne was impressed.

'Oh look – lashings of goji berries and unprocessed honey in this raw smoothie,' she trilled, feeling somewhat vindicated to have arrived on the other side of the world and found a place where everyone wanted to eat as healthily as she did.

Indeed, as Anne had decided to take a break from cooking for them all – she was yet to familiarise herself with the Australian fashion for electric stovetops – they were eating most of their meals at Burnt Sugar Love Goddess Gratitude, and so it was that they encountered their new neighbours as they were en route to the café for breakfast.

As the five tumbled out onto the footpath, famished after an early half-jog along the famous Bondi Beach, they stopped abruptly to avoid colliding with a fresh-faced bunch of three women and three men chattering loudly about the frustrations of being creatives.

'G'day,' said one of the young men, pushing a ridiculously long blond fringe out of his eyes, perhaps as a way of distracting them from the fact that he was not wearing a shirt. 'You the new neighbours?'

'Oh, hi!' said one of the young women perkily. 'I'm Tayluh! We heard youse had moved in!'

Julian blanched at what he had just heard: an assault on the English language by way of a plural pronoun that was not, in any way, acceptable to him. *Youse? YOUSE?*

'I'm Brodie,' said the first young man. 'These are my mates – Tayluh, a'course, and Harrison, Jazmin, Bindi and Reece. We're new in Bondi too. Just moved here from The Shire.' As he grinned his teeth were unexpectedly snow white. 'Where you from?'

'The United Kingdom,' George said stiffly while Dick wondered if they had somehow found themselves in a Tolkien half-world. *The Shire?*

'Oo-er,' said the one identified as Reece, whose hair was scraped up into a bun that would have made Dame Margot Fonteyn proud. 'Posh, are ya? Here's one – how can you tell if a plane is full of Poms?'

'How?' said Julian, always keen to learn something new.

'When the engines are off, you can still hear the whining! Hahahahahaha!' Reece's guffawing seemed disproportionate to the amount of humour in the joke. Indeed, Julian, Dick, Anne and George didn't think it was funny at all.

'Just teasin',' Reece said once he realised his audience was not with him.

Perhaps it had been Reece they had heard loudly drumming until late the previous night; they had already deduced that their new neighbours had a fondness for playing world beats accompanied by the burning of what George identified as Nag Champa incense. The experience had almost made four of them wistful for Neil and Tim's acoustic efforts; Timmy had already made it clear he missed the old house by disappearing for an hour and returning with a mouth full of biltong.

'Ever seen the show *Near and Far*?' Reece said now, naming one of Britain's favourite soap operas: a long-running

*The five's new home in North Bondi had a water view
from the corner of a bathroom window.*

Australian program that tended to captivate high-school students and retirees with its offering of permanently summery locales and perpetually youthful people.

'No,' George said.

'I have!' said Anne. 'And it's Dick's absolute favourite.'

Her smile was so guileless that Dick had to accept she was simply trying to be friendly rather than embarrass him. Nevertheless, his cheeks turned pink and he looked at his feet while shuffling on the spot.

'When I manage to see it,' he mumbled.

'Don't be silly! You come home early every day in time to watch it,' Anne gently chided.

The colour in Dick's face deepened but Reece merely looked delighted.

'A fan,' he said. 'Sweet. You might recognise these guys.' He motioned towards his companions. 'Jazmin, Harrison and Brodie are in the cast.'

Dick looked up and realised that, indeed, he did recognise them, and now he was in a quandary: to express the excitement he was suddenly feeling would reveal the depth of his long-lasting love for a show that his friends had left behind when they finished their A levels, but to not acknowledge that he recognised them would suggest Anne was lying about his devotion. It was the sort of exquisite paradox he had never expected to find himself in. He now regretted that he had not read Philosophy at the university to which he did not gain entry.

'Oh,' he said softly. 'Yes, I do. Hi.' He glanced at the *Near and Far* cast members quickly in turn, then looked at his feet again.

Julian took it upon himself to introduce the four of them – five, including Timmy – to their new acquaintances.

'So there are five of youse,' said Tayluh. 'And six of us.'

'How astonishingly perceptive of you,' said Julian, earning him an elbow in the side from George, although Tayluh didn't seem to have heard him. Instead, she looked as if a lightbulb had just gone off inside her hair extensions.

'We can be the Sydney Six,' she said. 'Y'know, because we're from Sydney.'

Julian believed he had caught the sound of a rising inflection at the end of her sentence. He'd heard rumours of their existence – from Bertie – but never witnessed one in the wild before. He was unaccountably thrilled.

'Do you have a nickname?' said Brodie, his hair back in his eyes. 'Seein' as yer a sort of tribe, like us?'

'Not really,' George said, frowning at Julian. She was sure he was going to make them look foolish, given half the chance.

'What do you mean, George?' Julian said blithely. 'We're the Famous Five!'

George looked like she wanted to dissolve into a puddle as Tayluh jumped up and down on the spot.

'That's awesome!' she declared. 'The Famous Five meet the Sydney Six!'

'And the five are hungry,' George snapped.

'We're having drinks later tonight,' Tayluh carried on as Julian felt a shiver of excitement at yet another rising inflection. 'We've had some frosés in the freezer for *evah*.' She rolled her eyes but George had no idea why: Tayluh was, as far as she could tell, being neither sarcastic or ironic, and those were the only reasons for eye-rolling.

George had further cause for alarm as Tayluh stepped closer to her. 'Wanna join us? We have some champagne too.'

'I suspect you mean sparkling white wine,' Julian sniffed.

'Oh, that would be smashing!' said Anne, although George's glare told her otherwise.

'Come on, Timmy,' George said, hoping to end any discussion of socialising she did not wish to engage in. These people were uncultured, unsophisticated and altogether not who she wanted to spend her time with. And what on earth were *frosés*?

Timmy, however, was far more interested in sniffing Jazmin's ankles, and George realised she had lost control of the situation. The only solution was to walk as briskly as she could to the café, order a soothing chia smoothie with raw cacao and shredded dates, and take her time to recover.

She did not wait to see if the others were following, but by the time she had ordered the smoothie the sound of high-pitched laughter was close, and she realised she would be forced to be cordial with these people, if only for Dick's sake. After all, only she knew that he had a poster of Jazmin on the back of his bedroom door at home.

CHAPTER SIX

A Wet and Wild Experience

'I can't see a *thing*,' Anne said with a tone as close to indignation as she had ever used in her life. 'The sun is *right in my eyes*.'

'What?' Julian said, barely able to hear her over the squawking of seagulls that had amassed around him ever since he had visited the fish-and-chip shop across the road.

'How are we going to even see these surfboards to get on them?' George moaned, wishing she had bought sunglasses after all. She had simply never needed them before – the English sun at its most powerful barely warranting a squint – but here in Australia, it was clear, her retinas were going to burn to a crisp if she didn't do something about it.

'You'll be right,' said Harrison cheerfully, taking off his shirt.

The five had gathered on the beach on the insistence of their new best friends, the Sydney Six. Over the previous week the five had been invited to the nightly 'creative infusions', as Bindi called them, that took place at the six's home. There the five had met a variety of soap opera actors – both currently employed and 'waiting for a call-back' – as well as models who declared they were about to move to New York and young men wearing their hair in what they called a 'man-bun' while sporting pants rolled higher on the ankle than Julian thought wise and thick beards they referred to as 'ironic Ned Kellys', plus various assorted others who all seemed to work in hospitality while insisting that they were creatives.

Creatives, indeed, appeared to make up the majority of the local population. Bindi, Reece and Tayluh were amongst their number, despite Bindi working at the local supermarket (Julian had noted the term 'checkout chick' so he could research it later), Reece as a bartender at the local pub, and Tayluh as a barista (although she pronounced it 'barrister') at a local café. It had taken the five only a short while to establish that their neighbours rarely left Bondi; indeed, they existed within a four-block radius.

In contrast, Jazmin, Harrison and Brodie worked in Sunshine Cove, the fictional location of *Near and Far*. One of the benefits of this location was that they were able to surf on their breaks, provided they did not stray within camera shot. As a consequence, all three were proficient surfers – and they were now intent on teaching the five to surf.

'So how many of you have surfed before?' said Brodie, glancing at each of them in turn, then taking a selfie as he stood with his surfboard before spending several minutes 'uploading', he said, so his 'fans' could have 'fresh content' (#surfsupyourenot).

That at least gave Julian some time to think of an excuse, for he didn't want to admit the truth: that he had surfed once, in Cornwall, and been very bad at it. He needed an excuse to avoid embarrassing himself in front of the Sydney Six, who could no doubt hang ten like professionals. Moreover, he knew that at his current weight he would look like a Yorkshire pudding floating on the water.

'None of us has,' Dick said, and Julian was glad he'd never told him about Cornwall.

'Wait,' said George, who had kitted herself in board shorts and a wetsuit-like top, clearly convinced that the water temperature was not the 22 degrees Celsius that the app on Brodie's smartphone said it was. 'What about Timmy? He can't stay alone on the beach.'

'I'll stay with him,' Julian volunteered, delighted that an excuse had so readily presented itself. He coughed unconvincingly. 'I think I'm coming down with a cold, so it's best I don't go in the water.'

'I think I'm coming down with a cold, so it's best I don't go in the water.'

'But you were in the water yesterday,' Dick said. 'You didn't even care about those shark sightings. That alarm went off and ...' He gasped.

'Honestly, Dick, not again,' Julian said impatiently.

'What is it?' said Jazmin with concern.

'After the alarm a helicopter flew low over the beach,' Anne said quietly. 'Checking for sharks, you know. It upset him. You see, there was an incident a few years ago. Prince Andrew was flying a helicopter around Dorset – he missed being in the Falklands War, apparently. He went to land in a field where Dick was walking and there was nearly a tragic accident.' She bit her lip and an awkward silence fell over the group.

'Shark sightings?' Harrison said, startling them all. 'They reckon that's some guy having a laugh. Swimming around with a fin on or something.'

'It's hardly funny,' George said sternly. 'I've seen *Jaws*.'

'And so have I.' Anne had turned a distinct shade of puce. 'Was that shark real?'

'Don't worry about it,' Reece said breezily. 'Been surfing here for months. Only sharks in the water are the dickheads who drop in on your wave. Come on. You can use our boards. I guess *Julia* can stay with the dog.' He smirked.

Julian's first instinct was to lecture Reece about his misapprehension that turning a man's name into a woman's was some kind of insult – Julian had recently developed a feminist consciousness and had realised a few home truths about the male of the species. But Reece's shoulders were twice as wide as his, and he was sure Reece had 5 per cent body fat to his 45, so he simply nodded and gestured to Timmy to follow him up to the boardwalk.

They could have their surfing, and he could keep his secret surfing past to himself, and they would all be content.

CHAPTER SEVEN

An Unexpected Encounter

While Julian was pleased to not be surfing, he was somewhat bored standing on the cement walkway behind the sand, trying not to let Timmy run away from him. He wasn't much interested in people-watching – he wasn't European, after all; he did not like to dine al fresco while strangers wandered by as if in a parade.

Instead he bought himself a salted caramel gelato from a little franchise shop and watched as several quite muscular men availed themselves of the workout equipment adjacent to the beach. *Pfft* – they didn't look that fit or strong. He was sure he could give them a run for their money. He'd just finish his gelato first.

'Cousin Julian!'

Perhaps he was so high on sugar that he was imagining things, for surely that voice belonged to their cousin Rupert Kirrin. Yet there was no way Rupert could be in Australia …

'I say, Cousin Julian!'

46

Julian blinked and turned towards the sound. There stood tall, handsome Rupert, dripping wet, wearing an item of swimwear that Julian had learnt were called 'budgie smugglers' in Australia and which he knew as 'Speedos', goggles pushed up on his forehead, and something strapped to his back. A fin.

'Cousin Rupert?' He narrowed his eyes in case this was an optical illusion.

'What are you doing here?' Rupert said, droplets of water splashing on Julian as he drew near. 'And Timmy?' Rupert arched an eyebrow then looked out to sea. 'Have you drowned the others?' His laugh was robust.

'No,' Julian said tightly. 'They're surfing.'

'Really?' Rupert now looked amused and Julian had an urge to punch him. He had long felt something more violent than ambivalence for his cousin, who somehow managed to insinuate himself into every situation.

'What are *you* doing here?'

'You answer me first.' Rupert said, unclipping his fin and throwing it to the ground at Julian's feet, so that water splashed all over Julian's pasty-white shins.

'We're having a gap … thing.'

'Is that all? I'm here to buy a media empire. I hear they're going for a song.' Rupert sniffed loudly and, Julian thought, a tad dismissively.

'A media empire?' Julian thought this sounded grandiose even for Cousin Rupert.

'A media empire?' Julian thought this sounded grandiose even for Cousin Rupert, who now waved his hand dismissively.

'Newspapers, television networks,' he said. 'You know. Whatever's going.'

'With what money?' Julian said. Rupert was forever doing exotic, expensive things with no visible source of income.

'Don't worry yourself about that. Now, how's Timmy, hm?' Rupert bent down to pat Timmy's head.

Julian rather hoped Timmy would bite him, except Timmy was known to have the most even temperament of them all.

'Nice that he didn't have to stay in Quarantine, wasn't it?' said Rupert, and a realisation suddenly dawned on Julian.

'You,' he said. '*You* were the one who smuggled him out.'

Rupert clicked his heels together like a von Trapp child and nodded enthusiastically. 'I did. Spied him there in the crate and couldn't help myself. No one likes to be caged, do they, boy?'

'Woof!' said Timmy.

'You'll just need to keep an eye out for Customs officials,' Rupert said, serious now. 'It's illegal to smuggle a dog in, you know.'

'I didn't do it!' Julian blustered. Honestly, Cousin Rupert was the worst human being he knew, always making other people pay for his actions.

Rupert winked. 'They don't know that, though, do they? Anyway, I'm off. I've got a meeting with a man about a loan. Cheerio.'

Julian opened his mouth to admonish his cousin but Rupert seemed to vanish. The only evidence that he had been there at all was the fin. The fin at his feet. The fin that looked as if it belonged to him just as the Sydney Six made their way up the beach, with Anne, George and Dick in tow, and Julian was forced to reckon with the shocked expressions of his sister, cousin, brother and new creative friends as they drew near.

CHAPTER EIGHT

Destination: Sunshine Cove

'Julian, how could you!'

If he lived to be a hundred Julian would never forget the look of disappointment, bordering on betrayal, on Anne's face as she saw the fin. For all his nonchalance about the feelings of others, it was Anne whom Julian secretly never wanted to let down – and now he had. Or she thought he had. All because of that dastardly Rupert.

'I didn't,' he hissed. 'It was Rupert.' Yet even as he said it, he knew how unlikely it sounded – even for Rupert.

George snorted. 'Of course. He just *happened* to be here.'

'He was!' Julian was indignant. They *knew* how appallingly bad Rupert could be – why was it so implausible that he had appeared in Bondi, half a planet away from home, and pretended to be a shark?

After several seconds of icy stares and pursed lips, with only Dick looking like he might be sympathetic to Julian's situation, Timmy resolved the matter by picking up the

Not at this age. He was meant to have a crush on Helen Mirren by now.

straps of the fin in his teeth, running down onto the sand and burying the offending object.

Later the five retired to their home and tried to recover from the events of the day. It seemed that Julian was not the only one to have had an awkward experience on the beach.

'I hate surfing,' Dick moaned.

'Yes, but you *love* Jazmin,' Anne said affectionately.

'What do you mean?' said Dick, panicking that she might have seen his poster. 'She's nice. Very nice. Awfully nice. That's all.' He knew his protests might alert Julian to the truth and perhaps provide fodder for future teasing, but he had to do something. He couldn't let them think he had a crush on a soap opera star. Not at *this age*. He was meant to have a crush on Helen Mirren by now.

'Oh, nothing.' Anne smiled and Dick immediately felt better. Anne would never tease him. 'I just noticed that you seemed very keen to keep getting on her board.'

Julian smirked and George glared at him.

'That's not a euphemism,' George said. 'It actually happened.'

'Anyway, I don't think she minded,' Anne went on. 'She said they could take us to Sunshine Cove tomorrow so Dick can practise his surfing there. Somehow she knew that he might like that.' Anne looked pointedly at George.

'I didn't say anything!' George protested.

'Oh darling, don't fib,' said Anne. 'You know that your right eye twitches when you do that.'

'All right, I might have said something,' George grumbled. 'It just slipped out.'

At this, Dick looked distraught. His addiction to watching *Near and Far* was a fact known only to Julian, Anne, George and Timmy. He had long feared that others would not understand – that they might even condemn him for it. For, after all, he was definitely not in that show's target demographic.

'Jazmin seemed quite pleased,' George said more brightly. 'I don't think she'd have offered to take us there otherwise.'

So it was that the next morning the five squashed into Jazmin's four-wheel drive, while the rest of the Sydney Six divided themselves between Harrison's and Brodie's off-road vehicles. Upon arrival at Sunshine Cove – which was not its real name but no one had the heart to tell Dick that – they joyfully sprang out of the car.

'Do you think we'll meet Ralph Ewart?' Dick said hopefully. Ralph Ewart was the quasi-legendary mainstay character of *Near and Far*, a curmudgeon given to phrases such as 'bloody oath' and 'strewth' (which George also liked to use on occasion). For a while Dick had incorporated such phrases into his day-to-day speech, until Julian, unable to

*Perhaps the fact that convicts had been allowed to run
wild out here meant that everything was freewheeling.*

take what he considered an abuse of the English language, had had a meltdown.

'Doubt it,' Harrison said, tearing off his shirt for no apparent reason. 'We only film out here on Mondays and Tuesdays.' He smiled, showing his unnaturally white teeth. 'And today's Friday.'

'You don't work on Fridays?' George said.

'Sure we do – if it feels right,' he said, then turned to gesture at his friends. 'But we're creatives. We go with the vibe. If we don't want to work, we don't.'

George had never met an employer who believed in such a philosophy, but perhaps things were different in the Antipodes. Perhaps the fact that convicts had been allowed to run wild out here meant that everything was freewheeling. She quite liked the idea; she had long suspected she was a blithe spirit trapped in a straitlaced life. She hadn't expected to find much in common with Australians but it seemed as if they might have a kinship after all.

CHAPTER NINE

A Day in the Sun

Dick insisted on wandering around the beach, nearby park and streets that made up the fictional Sunshine Cove, sure that Ralph Ewart could be encountered if only he looked hard enough. He set off on foot before the last car arrived, so he was not there to see Rupert Kirrin emerge from Brodie's Jeep.

Julian could not help the squawk he emitted upon sighting his unwelcome cousin.

'What are you doing here?' he said as he reached Rupert's side, hoping to spirit him away – perhaps dunk him under a wave – before Anne saw him.

Anne was prone to forgiveness; it was one of her many lovely qualities, but when it came to Rupert, Julian did not believe it was warranted.

'I'm auditioning for a part on *Near and Far* next week,' Rupert said, surveying the landscape as he spoke. 'I met Brodie here at the production office and he suggested I join your little expedition.'

As Rupert smiled, baring his perfectly even teeth, Julian silently cursed him: Rupert was so good-looking that he was a shoo-in to be cast in Dick's favourite television show, and there were several possible outcomes: that Dick would be so jealous he would lose his natural sunniness and sulk, which would not suit any of them; that he would stop watching *Near and Far* and be denied the great joy of his life; or that Rupert was likely to win the admiration of his co-star, and Dick's crush, Jazmin, simply because young women seemed to admire Rupert due to his intense masculinity and full head of hair. (Dick didn't think Julian knew about his poster of Jazmin, but he did.)

In short: Rupert's appearance at Sunshine Cove was a disaster, and there was only one way Julian could think of to deal with it.

'Fine,' he said. 'I'm going for a swim.'

As Julian stalked off to the beach, he could hear some shouting behind him and presumed it was the usual general merriment on the part of the Sydney Six. Alas, what he did not hear was their warning: there was a sign on the beach indicating that bluebottles were in the water. It took mere seconds for Julian to find that out for himself, and to discover that, despite their innocuous name, bluebottles could sting a man powerfully enough to make him weep.

He always found the classics to be a source of comfort in times of trouble.

'Holy Mother of Zeus!' he declared as a tentacle wrapped around his torso; he always found the classics to be a source of comfort in times of trouble.

He spent the next hour being tended to by Bindi and laughed at by Rupert, who was strutting around saying 'Flamin' galah' and 'Bloody drongo' as if he, not Ralph Ewart, was responsible for the phrases. Julian's pain, both from the bluebottle stings and his proximity to Cousin Rupert, was so intense that he failed to notice Timmy taking off for the sand dunes in the distance.

When George returned holding a fishing rod and a bucket, and wearing a smug grin – clearly, she had caught something – Julian was forced to tell her that her dog had disappeared.

'But I left him with *you*!' she cried.

'No, you didn't,' Julian blustered. 'I went for a swim. Blame Rupert – he was here too.' He looked around. 'In fact, he was the only one here.'

'Where's Anne?' George said, frowning.

So now Anne, Dick and Timmy were in parts unknown, which meant Julian and George were left to deal with Rupert and his new fans, the Sydney Six. Or, rather, Sydney Five. The shirtless Harrison had disappeared too.

'He followed Anne,' Reece said when they quizzed him. He winked. 'Think he's a bit sweet on her.'

'Can you help us find Timmy, then?' said George.

'Nah, sorry – I'm flat out like a lizard drinking.' Reece winked again, and Julian could not decide if he was trying to be flirtatious with George or was developing an inflammatory eye condition. Regardless, Reece's reply was unintelligible. They would have to find Timmy without him.

'I'll come!' volunteered Bindi.

'Me too,' said Tayluh.

The four trudged off up the beach, completely missing the spectacle of a brightly sunburnt Anne tidying her hair as she walked back towards the cars, trailed by a pleased-looking Harrison. For some reason she had failed to apply the SPF80 sunscreen she had repeatedly sworn she would slather on herself even during a solar eclipse.

Several hours passed before they all reunited. Some of them had found the site of the Sunshine Cove Café – a feature of the television show – and managed to feed and water themselves; indeed, their lips were still slick with the deep-fryer grease from the fish and chips they had consumed so eagerly. Others, by contrast, were thirsty and hungry.

But it was only when Dick trailed in, looking dejected, that Julian, Anne and George realised he'd had the worst day of them all.

'No Ralph Ewart?' Anne said sympathetically and Dick hung his head as he shook it.

'No,' he said mournfully. 'Just some surfers from Canada and some tourists from Wales.'

'Never mind, old chap,' Julian said, clapping his brother so forcefully on the shoulder that Dick winced.

'Woof!' they heard from close by. 'Woof! Woof!'

'Timmy!' George cried delightedly. 'At least we have you back!' She bent down to greet him and was mortified to see him run towards Rupert then roll over to expose his belly.

'Guess he knows who's alpha,' Rupert said cheerily, and Julian was pleased to see Anne, George and Dick looking murderously at him. So long as Timmy was the only family member who could tolerate Rupert, Julian could bear the drive home.

CHAPTER TEN

A View from Above

'I'm not going up there!' Dick said, clutching onto a railing on the Sydney Harbour Bridge, dressed in the grey overalls that were required of everyone who wanted to climb the massive iron span. The colour mystified Dick: they practically blended in with the grey paint of the bridge itself. What if a low-flying aircraft – such as a helicopter – was to decide to land on the bridge and landed on them instead?

'Dick, please!' Anne said, her hair whipping around her face. It really was one of her better attributes that she was so lacking in vanity she didn't mind her hair becoming a tangled mess in a high wind.

'Is it the overalls?' Julian said, plucking at his own. 'They are rather drab.'

'I quite like them,' George said. 'They're utilitarian.'

'Woof!' came a faraway contribution from Timmy, whom they had left behind in the offices of ClimbUp, the company that organised such expeditions and for which

Dick paused to gulp down a rising tide of panic. 'I think I'm scared of heights.'

Dick hoped to work as part of his gap-year plans. *Had* hoped to work, before he'd started this climb.

'Look at the view, darling!' Anne cried, sweeping one arm out in the manner of Julie Andrews on a hilltop. 'Isn't it extraordinary?'

Dick could have no opinion on the matter, for he was intent on looking only at the railing.

'I think—' Dick paused to gulp down a rising tide of panic. 'I think I'm scared of heights.'

'Don't be ridiculous,' Julian said, getting impatient. Dick was at the head of the queue so they were all stuck behind him, and Julian had plans to reach the summit of the bridge and declare himself king of the world, in the fashion of Leonardo DiCaprio, in different circumstances, in *Titanic*.

'You had no problem climbing trees when we were children,' said Anne soothingly.

'This is a considerably bigger tree!' Dick said, sounding alarmed.

So the climb was abandoned, along with Dick's gap-year job idea, and instead they decided to stroll around Circular Quay to the Opera House, where there were cafés that served caffè lattes. Dick had recently decided that the caffè latte was a much more rewarding drink than café au lait, and Anne was convinced that a soothing hot beverage was

65

just what he needed. What they all needed, since Julian was now in a snit.

They found a table outside at a venue that was crowded with people holding up smartphones – many of them attached to long poles that George had been reliably informed were called 'selfie sticks' – as if they were making offerings to an unseen god or charismatic leader. Only close observation of their hand movements revealed that they were, instead, taking photographs (#wowsydneywowwow).

'Should we take a photo?' Anne said as their beverages were served. 'A memento?'

'Of what – Dick's little fear of heights?' Julian said archly, craning his neck to observe the worshipping tourists.

'Don't be mean!' Anne said. 'You can climb the bridge another day. Dick's had a fright. We need to—'

'Oh!' Dick cried. 'Oh no!'

'What is it now?' Julian looked back to see George's eyes widening in what appeared to be her attempt to hold back laughter. He glanced at Dick and saw something dribbling down his forehead.

'A bird,' Dick moaned.

'A seagull,' George explained.

'It pooed on me,' Dick said sadly. 'Could this day get any worse?' He picked up his coffee and made a face. 'Ugh – this is your soy latte, George.'

He closed his eyes and thought about koalas.

George, with cup already to lip, looked regretful. 'Oh dear,' she said. 'This one's soy too.'

'They're both soy?' Dick said, sounding even more upset.

'Now, now,' Anne said, patting his hand, wanting to brighten him up. 'Let's think of something fun to do.'

A ferry chugged past them.

'I know!' she said. 'Let's get a ferry!'

'To where?' George said.

'Taronga Zoo?' Anne looked at each of them with question marks in her eyes. 'Perhaps we'll see a koala and a wombat.'

'Oh goodie,' Julian said, downing his espresso in one mouthful. 'Marsupials.'

They were pleased to discover that the ferry to the zoo was a regular service, and – after smuggling Timmy on board by pushing him between the legs of two tall Americans as they walked up the gangway – soon found themselves competing for seats with other smartphone-wielding tourists. As Dick refused to sit outside lest another bird make him a target, he gazed out of a window mournfully while the others attempted to restrain Timmy, who seemed to find the ferry more exciting even than a visit to Kirrin Island.

'Shark!' one of the tourists cried as they rounded the Opera House. 'Shark! Shark!' He was pointing over the bow. Throwing caution to the wind, Dick raced outside to see what the fuss was about.

'Bloody Rupert,' Julian muttered, although quite how their cousin had managed to swim out to the middle of the harbour was beyond him. Rupert was fit, but he had his limits.

In the commotion Timmy somehow manoeuvred himself up onto the bow's tip, as George resorted to yanking on his tail to pull him back just as Julian grabbed his hind legs.

'He's strong for an old fellow, isn't he,' Julian said, breathless with the effort.

'He's in better shape than you,' George retorted, then she stifled an uncharacteristic squawk as something that was less like Cousin Rupert and more like an actual shark swam by.

'Was that …' Dick swallowed and bit his knuckle.

'It was,' Julian said, nodding quickly. 'It was Jaws.'

At this Dick felt slightly faint and looked around for a place to sit. He closed his eyes and thought about koalas. They were meant to be friendly and cuddly – unlike sharks. And they would remain stationary long enough for someone to take a photo of him that he could upload to the social media account he had been neglecting ever since he had failed to work out how to activate international roaming.

CHAPTER ELEVEN

A Strange Smell and a New Plan

That evening, the Sydney Six appeared at the back door of
the five's house, holding what appeared to be joss sticks.
Julian wrinkled his nose.

'What is that foul smell?' he said, loudly enough so they
could hear. He had never learnt to modify his outbursts to
protect the feelings of others, and was far too old to start now.

'Sage,' Jazmin said, bouncing into the room. 'We're here
to perform a cleansing spell for Dick.'

George and Anne looked at each other in alarm, then
looked at Dick, who appeared not to have reacted at all.

'You're here to what?' George said, moving to stand in front
of her cousin in case this 'cleansing' was at all like the colonic
irrigation Cousin Rupert had once persuaded her to have.

'Cleanse him.' Jazmin waved the stubby implement in
her hand in Dick's direction.

'Jeez, mate,' said Brodie, close on Jazmin's heels, also
clutching some of this sage. 'We heard that a koala did a
wee on ya.'

70

Dick glanced up and the horror of the afternoon's events was plain to see on his face. He had not wanted to mention the incident again, yet somehow news had travelled to their neighbours. He glared at Julian, who shrugged.

'It just slipped out,' Julian said. *While I was trying to impress Bindi*, he might have added, but he had yet to alert his siblings and cousin to the fact that he was on the make with a member of the Sydney Six.

'And what does this cleansing spell have to do with Dick?' George said, not leaving Dick's side.

'A koala weeing on you is bad luck, right?' said Harrison, looking very serious for such a handsome young fellow.

'Yes,' said Bindi, simpering as she caught Julian's eye.

'Who says it's bad luck?' said Anne, aghast.

'Like, traditional beliefs and stuff,' said Tayluh.

Reece brandished a cigarette lighter and set the flame to his sage, then proceeded to light the others' sage sticks.

'Dick, you're not going to let them do this, are you?' said Anne.

'Strewth,' said George. 'That stuff stinks. Get it out of here.'

The six circled Dick and waved their sticks up and down. George and Anne were alarmed to see no reaction from him at all.

'Should we chant?' Bindi whispered to Jazmin.

'Chant what?' Jazmin whispered back.

'Doesn't matter,' Bindi said more loudly.

Suddenly Dick stood up. 'It's useless!' he declared, sounding more dejected than anyone had ever heard him. 'Everything's useless! Even the koala didn't like me! I should never have come to Australia.'

He sat down again and folded his arms.

'It's nothing like I dreamed,' he said quietly, his chin dropping towards his chest, although his eyes flickered towards Jazmin.

The Sydney Six exchanged glances while still waving their sage, causing the air to become thick in a way that Julian hadn't experienced since a friend of his had visited Cuba and returned with contraband cigars that a small group of them had smoked until they were sick, declaring they were 'taking one for Team Castro'.

'Maybe you need a change of scenery,' Jazmin said with a big smile.

'Yeah,' Brodie said. 'Sydney's not for everyone.'

'Some people like Melbourne,' Bindi said. 'It has culture. I think.'

'Some people like the Gold Coast,' Tayluh said, nodding slowly as if she had made a great discovery. 'It has, y'know, glamour and stuff.'

Julian, already bored, decided to move the conversation along.

'We live in London,' he said curtly. 'We don't need to visit another city.'

'We need an adventure,' George said, then looked surprised, as if she hadn't meant to say it.

'An adventure, eh?' Brodie said. He pushed his fringe out of his eyes in what might have been an attempt to look thoughtful. 'Well, my aunt and uncle have a sheep place. Near Wagga Wagga.'

'Wagga Wagga?' George said slowly. She was sure that was what Timmy's tail did when he was happy.

'It's about six hours away,' Brodie informed them, taking a selfie while holding the sage stick and going through his mysterious uploading ritual (#spelltime).

Six HOURS? They could drive from London to Paris in less time (via the Chunnel, of course). In fact, they had done so once, when Julian had bought an MG convertible in British racing green and wanted to take it 'for a little spin'. The car was so small that poor Timmy had had to be wedged at George's feet, where out of distress he had gnawed on her Stan Smiths, and by the time they boarded the Eurostar they were all car sick, a condition not improved by their train trip.

Once they'd reached Paris they were so distraught that Julian had decided to sell the car to a friend from school who happened to have an apartment on the Left Bank and

'Wagga Wagga?' George said slowly. She was sure that
was what Timmy's tail did when he was happy.

needed a little runabout to get to his country house near Aix-en-Provence. They'd taken the Calais ferry home and never spoken of it again.

If they were to spend another six hours in a car together, there was no guarantee that they would even want to stay related at the end of it.

But they had a mission: to cheer Dick up. Moreover, Anne could always be relied upon to keep everyone's spirits buoyant. And the Sydney Six had three four-wheel drive vehicles between them, all with roofs and recycled air, so it wasn't as if all eleven of them would have to cram into one car.

'When do we leave?' said George.

'Woof!' said Timmy, to the delight of the Sydney Six, who all engaged in chuckles.

'Looks like Timmy wants to go right now, eh, fella?' said Brodie.

'Woof! Woof!' Timmy replied.

'We'll leave at sparrow's fart,' said Harrison.

'At what?' said Anne, blushing. Her cheeks only became more inflamed when Harrison winked at her.

'Dawn,' he said. Then he took his sage stick and, followed by the others, left the five in a fug of smoke, with only a night's sleep separating them from a marathon drive in the company of six rather shallow Sydneysiders.

CHAPTER TWELVE

Welcome to the Bush

Julian, George, Dick and Anne found it hard to believe that in six hours of driving they could pass approximately three petrol stations and a sole café – requiring a detour through a one-willow-tree town called Jugiong, which sounded like the name of a misplaced sea mammal – yet there were at least fifty dead marsupials on the side of the road.

Timmy had hidden his head in his paws each time they passed another mangled kangaroo or wombat, clearly feeling something akin to sympathy, but that had not stopped Anne crying out in despair or the others feeling wretched. Well, everyone except Julian.

'Clearly they were too stupid to get out of the way,' he'd said.

'But that's Skippy the bush kangaroo!' Anne had cried.

'Don't be ridiculous,' George had said crossly. 'The real Skippy died years ago.'

Strangely, that answer had not satisfied Anne, and Dick too was looking somewhat upset. They had wanted to 'see the real Australia' but apparently the real Australia involved a large amount of roadkill.

At least they had almost certainly left Cousin Rupert behind in Sydney. They had inspected each of the cars before departure – much to the consternation of the Sydney Six – and he was nowhere to be seen.

Eventually they turned onto a gravel road then pulled up in front of a large house in the middle of a far larger paddock with a nearby windmill and what looked to be a body of water not too far beyond. None of the five had brought bathers, although Timmy, obviously, could do without.

'A windmill!' Anne exclaimed as they alighted.

'Yeah – doesn't work,' said Brodie, yanking their bags from the rear of the car. 'They have power lines now.' Strung between the trees was the evidence of a massive electricity supply system, ruining Anne's bucolic dream.

'That's a rather large swimming pool,' said George, gesturing to the water, which she could now see was brown in colour and distinctly uninviting.

Brodie laughed uproariously.

'That's a bore,' he said. 'Only things swimming in there are yabbies.'

'A bore?' said George, clearly perplexed.

'A noun that could be applied to everyone we have met in this country so far,' Julian said under his breath.

'Huh?' Brodie said.

'Never mind,' Julian replied loftily.

'And what are yabbies?' said Dick, and Anne was grateful that he was trying to make up for their brother's rudeness.

Honestly, Julian was becoming so irascible as he aged. Clearly he was eating too much cheese and it was not agreeing with him; she'd also caught him indulging in something called a 'potato scallop', which was a local delicacy in the form of a round, flat, fried medallion of root vegetable. He was having at least one a day. She'd tried to discourage him by using the old adage 'a moment on the lips, a lifetime on the hips' but he'd accused her of being a 'fat shamer' and stomped out of the house.

'Small creatures with nasty little claws,' Brodie had said before pulling out his smartphone, taking a selfie and uploading. The five waited patiently, as they had learnt to do.

'What's today's hashtag?' Dick asked, keen to support his new friend.

'It's, um ...' Brodie squinted at his phone. '#Outbacklife.'

'Oh, are we in the outback?' George said, looking excited. As a youngster she had watched a VHS copy of the television mini-series *The Thorn Birds* and she had harboured a yearning to see the outback ever since. Not that she'd ever admitted to watching it, nor did she understand why everyone thought Bryan Brown was so attractive.

'Not really.' Brodie grinned, and the five were confused. If this barren-looking place with its sparse trees, a swimming pool that couldn't be swum in, dirt roads and no other houses for ages wasn't the outback, what was it? And why was Brodie calling it that if it wasn't?

'It's the bush,' he explained.

'The ... bush?' Julian frowned. In his experience that word was used to refer to one item that belonged in a garden, not a whole property, or whatever this place was. He really needed to brush up on Australian etymology. Perhaps he could turn it into a PhD. It would be a good excuse to return to Oxford's bosom.

'Yeah, mate,' Brodie said. '"Outback" sounds cooler to my fans.'

The four-wheel drives containing the rest of the Sydney Six came roaring up to them, scattering gravel and making Anne cough.

'You're all over the place like a dog's breakfast!' Brodie called out to Harrison as he emerged from his vehicle. It was time to start carrying a notebook, Julian decided, so he could record all these bizarre phrases he kept hearing. Perhaps he could become the Sir David Attenborough of the language, boldly going where no Englishman had gone before.

'Sorry!' Harrison looked contrite as he saw Anne brushing dust off her dress.

'It's the bush,' he explained.

'Get a move on,' Brodie said. 'We've got some shearing to do.'

'Shearing?' Julian had no idea what this involved and was not sure he wanted to find out.

'Yeah, drongo. *Sheep* shearing.' Brodie turned and walked inside, followed by the other members of the Sydney Six, who were simultaneously uploading their #Outbacklife photos to their favourite social media platforms.

The five picked up their suitcases and followed the six into the house – and to the soon-to-be-revealed new adventure called shearing.

CHAPTER THIRTEEN

A Series of Unfortunate Incidents

'So this is my cousin Dale,' said Brodie, nodding at a young man who was wearing a battered hat – an 'Akubra', he had said, whatever that was – a tatty blue singlet and 'King Gees'. These, it seemed, were shorts. On his feet he wore 'Holeproofs' – a brand of sock advertised as being tough enough for a man to do without boots, yet Dale had decided to pair them with 'RMs'. All 'bushies' wore 'RMs', Brodie explained.

Linguistically Julian was finding this trip to the bush to be far more educative than their time in Bondi. Five minutes with Dale had already given him a cornucopia of possibilities for the PhD he was now determined to pursue. And it had distracted him from the mission at hand: to participate in the aforementioned shearing.

'Dale's gonna show us how to shear a sheep,' Brodie said, looking around at the other members of the Sydney Six and four of the five, Timmy having been tied up outside lest he agitate the flock. George had protested, saying they'd never tied Timmy up before, but Dale had been impervious. Or, rather, he'd been distracted by the sight of Bindi, Jazmin and Tayluh in their shorts and singlets. They, on the other hand, were busy taking selfies and discussing hashtags.

'Julian, George and Dick, you get to have a go,' said Brodie.

'What about me?' said Anne, looking quite put out.

'It's not for girls, love,' said Dale, tipping his hat to her.

'But what about George?' said Anne, confused.

'What about George?' Brodie said. His uncomprehending expression was matched by the rest of the six. Anne realised she shouldn't press the point. George would enjoy the shearing, she knew.

'So what will I do?' Anne said.

'I'll show you round the place,' Harrison said, stepping towards her. 'I don't really want to shear anyway.'

'What are ya, a big girl?' said Reece, sniggering, only to be met by glares from Julian, Dick and George.

'I find the casual sexism of men in this country to be nothing short of alarming,' Julian said in what sounded very much like a growl.

'What?' said Reece. 'What's wrong with saying that?'

Julian and George rolled their eyes, while Dick and Anne looked disappointed. Harrison, meanwhile, cleared his throat.

'Anne and I are going for a walk,' he announced, and the pair left the shearing shed.

'Hey, Reece,' said Dale.

'Yeah?'

'My dad needs a hand spreading manure on the canola fields.' Dale nodded his head in the direction of the house. 'Off ya go.'

George, Dick and Julian found it hard to suppress their amusement as Reece slunk away; even Timmy emitted what sounded like a bark of approval.

'Orright,' said Dale, who had briefly disappeared outside and returned clutching a large, woolly sheep. 'Brodie, hand me the shears, would ya?'

Dale then proceeded to show them how to hold the sheep and the shears, and how to move the shears deftly across the animal to produce what looked like a blanket of wool. The sheep, meanwhile, looked like it was being forced to spend an hour in the company of the new American president.

When he was finished, Dale stood up. 'See,' he said, wiping his brow with the back of his hand as sweat dripped onto his nose, 'easy.'

And Julian decided that it must be. Dale had done it so quickly, and if a man wearing a singlet with holes in it was able to achieve such a task, surely Julian could. He'd spent time in the country, after all – every time they camped

'I find the casual sexism of men in this country to be nothing short of alarming.'

on Kirrin Island they were technically 'roughing it', plus he'd driven past cows and horses, so he had experience with animals. A sheep was a third of his height and, as had become clear, quite slender underneath all that wool.

'I'll go first,' Julian declared, stepping towards Dale and holding out his hands for the shears.

Dale grinned, revealing a missing tooth. Julian was taken aback: where he came from, people went to an orthodontist if they had such problems.

'Onya, Jules,' Dale said, giving him the shears. Australians were, Julian had discovered, fond of shortening names wherever possible or, if it were not possible, they would lengthen them. Thus he had heard Dick called 'Dickie', George called 'George-oh' and Anne called 'Annie' – and he was 'Jules' or, once, 'Ju-ju', although he'd put a stop to that quick smart.

Julian rolled up his shirtsleeves – no need to drop standards or style here in the bush, and he had worn his favourite chinos, docksiders and linen shirt – and waited patiently as Dale retrieved a sheep.

Once the sheep was in his arms and he was bent over, about to use the shears, it became immediately apparent that while the animal was smaller than him, its kicking power was not dissimilar to that of a horse that had once presented a grave threat to his ability to father children when he walked behind it during a pony camp. He winced at the memory, and his momentary lapse of concentration allowed the sheep to butt its head up against his chin, knocking him unconscious.

When Julian came to, with Dick's and George's concerned faces above him, he immediately perceived that he had failed to shear the sheep. He could hear Timmy barking and thought how lovely it was that even their dog was worried about him.

'Get out of it!' he heard Dale yelling, and he wondered if that was a command to him, to get to his feet and leave.

'What's going on?' George said as she stood up and walked to where Dale was standing, looking out of the shed. There, she saw Timmy eyeing off a funny-looking, stocky little dog with patches all over it.

'What sort of dog is that?' she asked.

'Blue heeler,' Dale said. 'One of my best working dogs.' He looked wistful. 'Saved her life once.'

'How?' George said.

'She keeled over. Heart attack or something.' Dale wiped a tear from his eye. 'I gave her mouth-to-snout resuscitation.'

George recoiled at the idea of putting her mouth anywhere near a dog's snout. As much as she loved Timmy, it was perhaps a bridge too far for her to travel. Yet even as she thought it, her devotion to Timmy was put to the test as she suddenly observed what looked like the blue heeler attempting to round Timmy up as if he was a sheep, and Timmy, in his attempt to get away, pulling on the rope that tethered him to a stake in the ground.

Within seconds – far too quickly for George to react – Timmy had pulled the stake out of the ground and was taking off at speed, pursued by the barking blue heeler.

'Timmy!' George cried.

'Woooooof!' was the only response.

Clearly, the day was not turning out well for any of them.

CHAPTER FOURTEEN

Anne Does Not Find a Koala

'What on earth is this contraption?' said Anne, puzzling over the vehicle before her.

'Quad bike,' Harrison said, swinging one of his long, perfectly formed legs over it and nodding to the seat behind him. 'Hop on.'

'Can we not ride a horse instead?' Anne would always prefer a horse to a motorbike of any sort – reading *Black Beauty* ten times had had a lasting effect.

'A horse? Would you like a cart to go with it?' Harrison seemed to think this was hilarious, and Anne felt herself falter. For, if truth be known, Dick was not the only one who wanted to spend time with a cast member of *Near and Far*.

Unbeknownst to her brother, Anne was fond of catching up on episodes of the soap opera on her favourite streaming service, and she had developed as much of an interest in visiting the country of its setting as he had. She had recognised Harrison immediately when they had met but had played it cool – an ability she had never known she possessed. She was quietly thrilled that Harrison now seemed to have developed an interest in her, and had been only too pleased when he had suggested they go for a walk.

That walk had now become a veritable adventure to a destination unknown. If this trip Down Under had not turned out quite the way the others expected, to her mind it was very nice indeed.

Harrison stopped the quad bike beside another large body of water.

'Oh, I know what this is!' Anne exclaimed. 'It's a bore.'

'Close,' Harrison said, and Anne admired the way his thick hair had become ruffled in the breeze while they were on the bike. 'It's a billabong.'

'A billa-what?'

'Billabong.' Harrison stepped closer to her, and Anne, suddenly feeling an attack of modesty, moved closer to the billabong.

'And are there yabbies in this billabong?' she said, peering into the water.

'Probably,' Harrison said, and as Anne turned to look at him she recognised the expression on his face: it was the same one he made on television right before he passionately kissed a nubile co-star who would then slap him and say, 'I can't believe you'd do that, Jaxon!'

'Would you show me?' she said gaily, to cover her discomposure.

At that moment they heard loud cries from the tree branch above them. They looked up to see three kookaburras perched next to each other, in full voice.

'They're so *noisy*,' Anne said, putting her hands over her ears. She glanced up and saw them peering down at her as they continued to make a cry that sounded very much like a cackle.

'Are they ...' She gulped. 'Are they *laughing* at me?'

At this the birds swooped down towards her and Anne, faced with no other prospect of safe harbour, found herself in Harrison's strong, toned arms.

'No one,' he murmured, gazing down at her, 'would ever want to laugh at you.'

Anne gulped again. Here she found herself inside the very scenario she had sometimes allowed herself to daydream about: *Near and Far*'s Jaxon in the flesh, holding her close to him.

It wasn't that she hadn't had other close encounters – plenty of Julian's friends had asked her out and made promises that she could be Marchioness of Such-and-such and have a holiday house in Mustique and winters skiing in the Italian Alps and mini-breaks in Liechtenstein. But in truth, no one's company interested

91

She gulped. 'Are they laughing at me?'

her so much as that of her brothers and cousin. And Timmy. Dear Timmy.

No. It was simpler – perhaps even preferable – to keep Jaxon/Harrison as a daydream.

'Oh look,' she said, pointing up. 'Is that a koala?'

Before he could respond she extricated herself from his arms and used the skills she had learnt in a recent rock-climbing class to shimmy up the tree faster than anyone could say 'Vegemite'.

It wasn't until she had reached the high branches that she realised she had no idea how to get down.

CHAPTER FIFTEEN

Close Encounters with Dangerous Wildlife

Julian was feeling distinctly out of sorts after his encounter with the sheep, and in need of a loo.

The nearest facility, Brodie informed him, was the 'dunny' next to the shed. 'Dunny' appeared to be a synonym for 'outhouse', although Julian failed to detect a relationship between the two words. No mind – as long as the dunny flushed, that was all that concerned him.

'Watch out for the redback on the toilet seat,' Bindi said, her laugh tinkling as she took a photo of him opening the dunny door. Julian, his interest in her most definitely on the wane, was almost overcome with the impulse to flush her smartphone down the loo, and he had no idea why she needed to warn him about the toilet's decor.

Indeed, as he closed the dunny door he saw that the toilet's lid – or back, he supposed, in the vernacular – was black. If he'd earlier suspected that for all her appealing physical qualities Bindi was a little empty-headed, he was convinced of it now.

Julian was starting to suspect that as well as creatives they might be hipsters.

He lifted the lid and dropped his chinos. It was only then that he noticed a rather large black spider with a red stripe on its back, sitting underneath the toilet's rim.

There were moments in life, Julian knew, when one was confronted with choices. The choice to do good or bad; to be a man of principle or one who counted cards on a boys' weekend to Las Vegas; to be a caring brother or one who taunted Dick about his love for *Near and Far*.

Now he faced another difficult choice: run out of the dunny with his chinos down, or take the time to pull them up and risk being attacked by the spider. He'd heard about Australian spiders. They were smaller than those horrible bird-eating spiders in South America but more aggressive and deadlier than any in the world. It was a curious paradox in a country that had a similar land mass to the continental United States with a population that had a reputation for being relaxed to the point of catatonia.

Julian decided on a compromise, and elected to pull up his pants as he burst out of the dunny door.

'That was quick,' Brodie said.

'I'm a man of action,' Julian muttered, hoping that would be the end of the matter, but he caught a look of admiration mixed with desire on Brodie's face. Oh no, not again – he'd already had his friend Rafe falling in love with him, and it was a complication he did not need.

Besides, he wasn't that impressed with Brodie: the other day Julian had spotted a tattoo on the inside of his wrist, of the word 'COVFEFE', and when Julian had pressed him for an explanation the young man had, ridiculously, said it was 'ironic'. Everything Brodie and his friends did seemed to be 'ironic' and Julian was starting to suspect that as well as creatives they might be hipsters – a breed he loathed after a close encounter with some men wearing neckerchiefs and leather shoes without socks in a gastropub in Shoreditch.

'Let's go get some eggs from the coop,' Brodie said, and Julian wondered if that was some kind of euphemism.

'Oh yeah! The coop!' squealed Bindi, and she and Jazmin started skipping towards a haphazard contraption that George, Dick and Julian could now see was home to several sorry-looking hens.

'Would you like to get yolked?' Tayluh said, sidling up to George, who had no idea what she was talking about, and told her so before pushing open the wire and entering the coop.

'Wait!' Jazmin said, sounding panicked.

'What is it?' Julian said.

'Snake!' Brodie cried.

'Really?' said Dick, walking closer to the coop. 'What kind?'

'So what should I do?' said George, who was closest to
the snake but, as usual, unflappable in a crisis.

'Dick, stop,' said Julian sternly. 'I don't think it's like your pet python.' After leaving school, in a flush of adult responsibility, Dick had bought himself a pet. Anne and Julian, too, feeling that pet ownership was a hallmark of adulthood, had acquired a guinea pig and small parrot respectively. Unfortunately, Dick's pet had eaten Anne's and Julian's pets, which was why George alone had a pet.

'Um, it's a brown snake,' Brodie said, contorting himself so he could look more closely while remaining as physically distant as possible.

'Is that bad?' Dick said.

'They're one of the most venomous snakes in the world,' Tayluh whispered.

'So what should I do?' said George, who was closest to the snake but, as usual, unflappable in a crisis. 'Should I retreat?'

'No!' cried Tayluh. 'I don't want you to get bitten!' George appreciated the sentiment but not the histrionics with which it had been delivered, so she turned to her cousins for advice.

'Julian, what do you think?'

Having never previously needed to learn about how to manage venomous snakes, Julian shrugged.

'Dick?'

'Hit it with a stick?' Dick said, bending down to pick up a large specimen. 'That should give it a fright.'

'Don't be *stupid*,' Jazmin said, and Dick was horrified that the woman of his dreams was admonishing him.

'That'd just make it mad,' Brodie explained.

'Shall we run?' Julian said. 'Not you, George, obviously – but the rest of us could get away.'

It was not the first time George had given him a withering glance, but the impact of such glances never lessened.

The discussion about how to handle the snake lasted for another four minutes, during which time the reptile slithered on its way unmolested, while Julian and George's relationship grew more fractious than it had been when Julian had tried to interfere with George's sovereignty over Kirrin Island.

It was up to Dick to play peacemaker, although he dearly wished that his sister was there – Anne always knew the right things to say when George and Julian were at loggerheads.

The unpleasantness was only interrupted by the arrival of Harrison on the quad bike, alone. Anne was stuck up a tree, he said. After expressing surprise that Anne would even make it as far as a lower branch – out of all of them, she was the least accomplished tree climber – George, Julian and Dick set off on foot to rescue her.

CHAPTER SIXTEEN

The End of #Outbacklife

'Have you really not seen Timmy?' said Anne, sounding concerned but looking surprisingly unruffled after her close encounter with a eucalyptus. She had managed to get herself out thanks to an excellent distraction technique: Julian and Dick had remembered that a rousing round of 'Good King Wenceslas' always helped her to focus, and by the time they reached the middle of the second verse her feet had touched the ground, to a loud cheer from all present.

Nightfall had come and gone, and there was still no sign of the dog. Dale had expressed his annoyance that his best working dog was AWOL, as he called it, and George, too, was annoyed as she recalled the last time Timmy had disappeared overnight, when he was a younger dog in Dorset. They had found him curled up with a neighbour's toy poodle looking quite pleased with himself.

'No, we can't find him,' George said, polishing off the last of the fried eggs Dale had made them for breakfast. The eggs were delicious, despite the fact the yolks were an almost fluorescent green, a result of Dale feeding the hens grass cuttings in an attempt to replicate Dr Seuss's 'green eggs and ham'.

'I'd really rather not stay here much longer,' Julian said. 'I feel Bondi has more to offer us than the bush.'

He tasted the cup of instant coffee that Bindi had made for him and almost gagged. What he wouldn't have given for a proper espresso.

Dick, too, was keen to return to Sydney: after doing some research — mainly by inspecting Jazmin's *Near and Far* production schedule — he believed he could arrange to accidentally-on-purpose encounter Ralph Ewart after all.

'We can't leave without Timmy,' George said. 'And we need someone to drive us back.'

'I'm over it,' Tayluh announced as she pulled up a chair immediately adjacent to George's. 'This place sucks.'

'I agree,' said Reece, slurping his tea. 'It's as dry as a dead dingo's donger — my allergies are playing up like a footy team on Mad Monday.'

Reece illustrated his point by rubbing his nose with his hand.

'I think it's not too bad,' said Harrison, turning his megawatt smile on Anne, who blushed and looked away.

'We've got work tomorrow anyway,' said Jazmin.

Work? At this, Julian, Dick, George and Anne remembered

that they really should find jobs of their own. As much as this detour to the bush had been interesting, it was time to move on. But they couldn't leave without Timmy.

'Woof!'

With a delighted smile, George leapt to her feet.

They all ran to the kitchen door and saw Timmy walking slowly towards the house, with the blue heeler close behind him. But not chasing him.

'Those two look like they're getting along better,' said Dick.

'Is Timmy ... smiling?' said Julian.

'No!' George said, bending down to greet Timmy, hoping she could quickly spirit him away from that hussy of a blue heeler before any more damage was done.

Soon Brodie appeared and said he too was keen to return to Bondi, as he'd agreed to take part in a fire-twirling hula-hoop yoga festival on the beach early that evening.

'You could come with me,' he said hopefully to Julian, who informed him that he'd never twirled fire or hooped hulas in his life, and he didn't intend to start now.

After twenty minutes spent taking and uploading #Outbacklife selfies, the five packed themselves into Brodie's car once more. Before departure they agreed to let the Sydney Six take a detour to Canberra, the nation's capital, reprising their Year Six school trip when they'd sat

He'd agreed to take part in a fire-twirling hula-hoop yoga festival on the beach early that evening.

in the public gallery of parliament during Question Time and then all pursued Prime Minister John Howard for his autograph.

That in turn had sparked a robust conversation about something called the NBN; the case for annexing New Zealand or, alternatively, selling Tasmania to it; something about a political party for motoring enthusiasts, which sounded abjectly absurd; and the prospects of popular cricketer and former Elizabeth Hurley fiancé Shane Warne becoming Australia's first president.

'He'll spin us right,' said Reece, who appeared to be unreasonably self-satisfied with his play on words.

While the five were impressed that the six were so engaged in politics, they were relieved that the most they had to worry about at home was the Brexit vote. Life in the Antipodes was not as carefree as they'd expected.

Nor were the six as politically inclined as it had first appeared. As they passed the turn-off to the Barton Highway, which would take them to Canberra, Brodie wrinkled his nose and barely eased his foot off the accelerator.

'There's really nothing more to see there,' he said. 'I did it all as a kid. Questacon, Phar Lap's heart, that Carillon thing.' He sighed as if remembering something unpleasant, but as the five had no idea what he was talking about, they ignored him.

They continued their journey north, utterly failing to notice that an official-looking car had taken the same turn-off they had rejected, bearing as its passenger one Rupert Kirrin, media baron, on his way to make demands of Prime Minister and Cabinet, as was the national custom.

Upon arrival in Bondi, the five immediately felt relieved to be back near the beach, far from sheep and snakes. They were so pleased that they almost considered joining Brodie at his little festival, but decided instead to partake of caffè lattes at Burnt Sugar Love Goddess Gratitude, which gave them a chance to reflect on their experiences thus far.

They knew that their previous dissatisfaction had not been Bondi's fault. They had expected Australia to provide something to them without any effort on their part. The reality was that they would have to earn their right to an Australian adventure.

Starting tomorrow, Julian would look for work as a fruit-picker; Anne was going to learn how to become a barista; George was to seek employment as a bouncer at the nearest hotel; and Dick ... That was the very best part of the story: with help from Jazmin, Dick had secured the job of production dogsbody on the set of *Near and Far*.

This gap-year business was looking up already.